JEALOU

Published in paperback in 2019 by Wayland

Text copyright © Wayland 2017
Illustrations copyright © Mike Gordon 2017

Wayland
Carmelite House
50 Victoria Embankment
London EC4Y 0DZ

Wayland Australia
Level 17/207 Kent Street
Sydney, NSW 2000

Managing editor: Victoria Brooker
Creative design: Paul Cherrill

ISBN: 978 1 5263 0076 8

Printed in China

FSC
www.fsc.org

MIX
Paper from
responsible sources
FSC® C104740

Wayland is a division of
Hachette Children's Books,
an Hachette UK company.
www.hachette.co.uk

feeling JEALOUS!

Written by
Kay Barnham

Illustrated by
Mike Gordon

WAYLAND

"It's NOT fair," said Martha, punching a pillow. "What's not fair?" Lucy asked gently. She was Martha's best friend, but even she was a little scared of how cross Martha looked right now.

"Samuel goes to bed at eight o'clock,"
huffed Martha, hurling a cuddly hippo
across the bedroom, "and I have
to go at seven. See? *Not fair.*"
"Ah," said Lucy. She did see.

"Mum says I'm silly to feel jealous," added Martha.
"She says that Samuel's older than me,
so of course he should go to bed later."

Lucy thought for a moment.
Then she smiled. If Martha could think of
something good about being the younger one,
then she might feel happier.

"Doesn't Samuel have to unload the dishwasher?" said Lucy.

"Yes," said Martha, looking puzzled.

"And does he put the rubbish out too?" Lucy went on.

"Er, yes," said Martha, beginning to smile. "Mum says he has to do more jobs because he's older..."

Lucy grinned. "Actually," said Martha with a giggle,
"I don't like going to bed earlier than Samuel,
but I'm not at all jealous about his extra jobs."

At school the next day, George was showing off about his new hoverboard. "It's the best thing ever," he told anyone who would listen. "It's just like flying!"

"I wish he'd shut up about the stupid hoverboard," Katie muttered to Lucy.

"I want one really badly, but my mum says they're too expensive. It's not fair!"

Lucy wondered how she could make Katie look on the bright side. "Maybe you've got a toy that George doesn't have?" she suggested.

"I've got a skateboard," Katie said,
kicking a stone. "It's a bit like a hoverboard.
I suppose I could play with that instead ..."

"... while you're saving up,"
finished Lucy, with a wink.

A smile tugged at the corner of Katie's
mouth. It grew bigger and brighter
and Lucy couldn't help smiling back.

"I could, couldn't I?"
Katie said.

"It would take a long,
long time, but I could
save up and buy my
own hoverboard!"

15

After school, Lucy and her brother Alex went
to visit their Auntie Linda, who had just adopted
a scruffy old terrier called Bob.

"Bob is unbelievably cool," sighed Alex,
rubbing the dog behind the ears.
He loved animals so much.
He wanted to be a vet
when he grew up.

Lucy held her breath.
She knew exactly what
was coming next ...

"I want a dog," said Alex. "Or a cat.
Or a hamster. I'd even settle for a gerbil.
I'd look after it really well. Why won't Mum
and Dad let us have one?" he moaned.

"Erm ... because Dad's allergic?" Lucy said quietly.
Dad sneezed if he even looked at a furry animal.
Alex knew this, of course. But it didn't stop him
being jealous of everyone who had a pet.

"Auntie Linda," said Lucy, stroking the little dog, "do you think we might be able to take Bob for walks?"

"Could we sort of *share* him?"

"What a wonderful idea!" said Auntie Linda.
"Why don't we start now?"

And she handed the lead to Alex,
who beamed with happiness.

The following week, it was the school sports' day. Lucy was so excited. She would win every race for her team! Her friends' cheers would be

DEAFENING!

Even better, her parents were coming to watch Lucy and her brother take part.

They would be so proud!

But Lucy dropped her egg 27 times in the egg-and-spoon race.

In the sack race, she fell on her face.

In the hurdles race, there wasn't a single hurdle standing when she finished ... in last place.

"Look, Alex is in the hurdles race,"
Martha said to Lucy. "That'll cheer you up.
Your brother's *so* fast."

Alex *was* fast. He was so fast that he finished in first place. Then he won the 100-metre race too.

Lucy scowled. Alex had done exactly what *she'd* wanted to do. He'd won. Now everyone was cheering *him!*

"Cheer up, Lucy," Martha said. "I know losing is hard, but the good thing is that your brother did so well."

Lucy saw Alex's shining face.
"I'll try to feel happy for him," she said.

"Besides, Alex is in the athletics team,"
Martha went on. "Why don't you take up a sport?
Then we could be cheering you next year."
Lucy thought for a moment.
She did love swimming ...

"Go on, have one of my medals," said Alex, hanging a medal around Lucy's neck. Lucy smiled at how everyone had bounced her own advice back at her.

And perhaps it was good advice, because now she didn't feel jealous at all.

FURTHER INFORMATION

THINGS TO DO

1. Green is a colour that is often linked with jealousy and envy. And so jealousy is sometimes known as the green-eyed monster... Can you draw or paint a picture of your own green-eyed monster? Make sure it looks super jealous!

2. This book shows lots of things that people might be jealous about, such as older brothers and sisters, toys, pets and success. What other things can you think of?

3. Make a colourful word cloud! Start with 'jealous', then add any other words this makes you think of. Write them all down using different coloured pens. More important words should be bigger, less important words smaller. Start like this...

I WANT THAT!

Jealous envy

NOTES FOR PARENTS AND TEACHERS

The aim of this book is to help children think about their feelings in an enjoyable, interactive way. Encourage them to have fun pointing to the illustrations, making sounds and acting, too. Here are more specific ideas for getting more out of the book:

1. Encourage children to talk about their own feelings, if they feel comfortable doing so, either while you are reading the book or afterwards. Here are some conversation prompts to try:

What makes you feel jealous?
How do you stop feeling jealous when this happens?

2. Make a facemask that shows a jealous expression.

3. Put on a feelings play! Ask groups of children to act out the different scenarios in the book. The children could use their facemasks to show when they are jealous in the play.

4. Hold a jealous-face competition. Who can look the MOST jealous?! Strictly no laughing allowed!

BOOKS TO SHARE

A Book of Feelings by Amanda McCardie,
illustrated by Salvatore Rubbino
(Walker, 2016)

Dinosaurs Have Feelings, Too: Jamal Jealousaurus
by Brian Moses, illustrated by Mike Gordon
(Wayland, 2015)

I Feel Jealous by Brian Moses, illustrated by Mike Gordon
(Wayland, 1994)

Not Fair, Won't Share by Sue Graves,
illustrated by Desideria Guicciardini
(Franklin Watts, 2014)

The Great Big Book of Feelings
by Mary Hoffman, illustrated by Ros Asquith
(Frances Lincoln, 2016)

The Lion, the Witch and the Wardrobe by C S Lewis
(HarperCollins Children's Books, 2009)